C0-AKJ-964

Moncure          JUVENILE          238072
J This book may be kept
          21 DAYS          READERS
A fine will be charged for each day the
book is kept overtime.

DISCARD
TAYLOR MEMORIAL LIBRARY

JUVENILE

READERS

**Taylor Memorial Public Library**
CUYAHOGA FALLS, OHIO
The Wm. A. and Margaretta Taylor
Memorial Association

DEMCO

# WORD BIRD'S CHRISTMAS WORDS

J·E
Mon
Ve

by Jane Belk Moncure
illustrated by Vera Gohman

Created by

THE
CHILD'S
WORLD

Distributed by CHILDRENS PRESS ®
Chicago, Illinois

Taylor Memorial Public Library
Cuyahoga Falls, Ohio

**CHILDRENS PRESS HARDCOVER EDITION**
ISBN 0-516-06574-2

**CHILDRENS PRESS PAPERBACK EDITION**
ISBN 0-516-46574-0


**Library of Congress Cataloging in Publication Data**

Moncure, Jane Belk.
  Word Bird's Christmas words.

  (Word house words for early birds)
  Summary: Word Bird puts words about Christmas
in his word house—North Pole, reindeer, candy canes,
stockings, and others.
    1. Vocabulary—Juvenile literature.
2. Christmas—Juvenile literature.   [1. Vocabulary.
2. Christmas]   I. Gohman, Vera Kennedy, 1922-      ill.
II. Title.   III. Series: Moncure, Jane Belk.   Word house
words for early birds.
PE1449.M527  1987          428.1          86-31666
ISBN 0-89565-361-3

© 1987 The Child's World, Inc.
All rights reserved. Printed in U.S.A.

1 2 3 4 5 6 7 8 9 10 11 12 R 95 94 93 92 91 90 89 88 87

# WORD BIRD'S
# CHRISTMAS WORDS

# Word Bird made a...

word house.

"I will put Christmas
words in my house,"
he said.

238072

# He put in these words—

Dear Santa,
I have
been a very
good bird.
Ple

Santa Claus
North Pole

# letter

# North Pole

# Santa's workshop

elves

reindeer

sleigh

# Santa Claus

# Christmas trees

balls

star

# candles

# carolers

# jingle bells

# Christmas cookies

# candy canes

# toy store

wrappings

gifts

# Christmas cards

mistletoe

poinsettias

holly

# Christmas flowers

238072

# stockings

# Christmas story

# silent night

# Merry Christmas

letter

Santa Claus

North Pole

Christmas tree

Santa's workshop

star

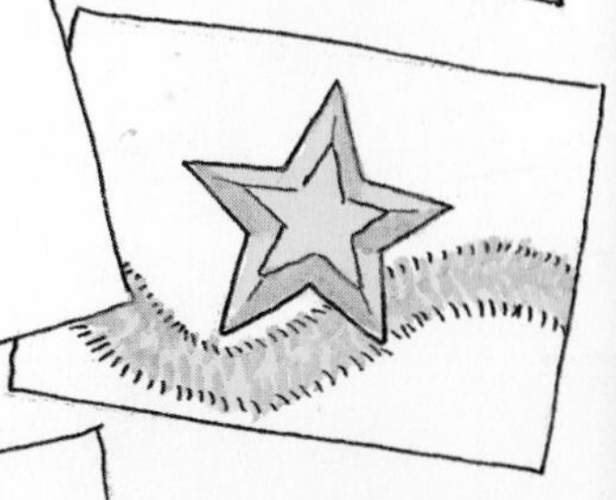

elves

candles

reindeer

carolers

sleigh

jingle bells

hristmas words with  ?

Word Bird

Christmas cookies

candy canes

Christmas flowers

toy store

stockings

gifts

Christmas story

The Night Before Christmas

wrappings

silent night

Christmas cards

Merry Christmas

December 25

You can make a Christmas word house. You can put Word Bird's words in your house and read them too.

Can you think of other Christmas words to put in your word house?